BILL EVANS

THIS ESSENTIAL NEW FOLIO REFLECTS THE UNIQUE TALENT
OF AN INNOVATIVE & EXTRAORDINARILY GIFTED MUSICIAN
FOURTEEN CLASSICS EDITED & TRANSCRIBED BY JACK LONG

JAZZ PIANO

WISE PUBLICATIONS
LONDON · NEW YORK · PARIS · SYDNEY · COPENHAGEN · MADRID

Exclusive Distributors:
MUSIC SALES LIMITED
8/9 Frith Street, London W1V 5TZ, England.
MUSIC SALES PTY LIMITED
120 Rothschild Avenue, Rosebery, NSW 2018, Australia.

Order No. AM91954
ISBN 0-7119-4070-3
This book © Copyright 1996 by Wise Publications

Music edited & transcribed by Jack Long
Music processed by Enigma Music Production Services
Compiled by Peter Evans

Book design by Pearce Marchbank, Studio Twenty
Computer production by Ben May

Photographs courtesy of
David Redfern/Redferns

YOUR GUARANTEE OF QUALITY

As publishers, we strive to produce every book to the highest commercial standards.
The music has been freshly engraved and the book has been carefully designed
to minimise awkward page turns and to make playing from it a real pleasure.
Particular care has been given to specifying acid-free, neutral-sized paper made from pulps
which have not been elemental chlorine bleached. This pulp is from farmed sustainable forests
and was produced with special regard for the environment.
Throughout, the printing and binding have been planned to ensure a sturdy,
attractive publication which should give years of enjoyment.
If your copy fails to meet our high standards, please inform us and we will gladly replace it.

Music Sales' complete catalogue describes thousands of titles and is
available in full colour sections by subject, direct from Music Sales Limited.
Please state your areas of interest and send a cheque/postal order for £1.50 for postage to:
Music Sales Limited, Newmarket Road, Bury St. Edmunds, Suffolk IP33 3YB.

VISIT THE INTERNET MUSIC SHOP
http://www.musicsales.co.uk

Also available...

COUNT BASIE JAZZ PIANO.
Seventeen superb piano arrangements by Stephen Duro, including
Lil' Darlin', Splanky, The Big Walk and Vine Street Rumble.
Order No. AM91951.

DUKE ELLINGTON JAZZ PIANO.
Seventeen classic jazz pieces arranged for solo piano by Stephen Duro,
based on original recordings of the Duke Ellington Orchestra.
Includes: Caravan, I'm Beginning To See The Light,
Perdido, Satin Doll and Take The 'A' Train.
Order No. AM91952.

JAZZ CLUB PIANO SOLOS: VOLUME ONE.
Fifteen great standards arranged for piano in jazz style by Steve Hill,
including A Night In Tunisia, Come Fly With Me, Fascinating Rhythm,
So Nice and That Ole Devil Called Love.
Order No. AM91544

JAZZ CLUB PIANO SOLOS: VOLUME TWO.
Twelve jazz standards arranged by Stephen Duro, including
Fever, Lazy River, Let's Get Away From It All,
Quiet Nights Of Quiet Stars (Corcovado) and Walkin' Shoes.
Order No. AM92014.

JAZZ CLUB PIANO SOLOS: VOLUME THREE.
Twelve all-time jazz favourites arranged by Stephen Duro, including
Georgia On My Mind, Lullaby of Birdland, Night Train, Sunny and Sophisticated Lady.
Order No. AM92015.

THE BEATLES FOR JAZZ PIANO.
Eleven classic Beatles songs arranged in jazz style for piano by Steve Hill,
including All My Loving, Eleanor Rigby, Michelle and Yesterday.
Order No. NO90504.

ELTON JOHN JAZZ PIANO
A dozen of Elton John's greatest hits arranged in jazz style by Jack Long.
Includes Candle In The Wind, Daniel, Goodbye Yellow Brick Road,
Sacrifice and Song For Guy.
Order No. AM935891

BILL EVANS: THE INFLUENTIAL INNOVATOR

At one time it used to be said, disparagingly, by people who should have known better, that Bill Evans was in reality not a jazz player at all. He was, they claimed, no more than a superior kind of cocktail pianist.

Though somewhat misguided, it's easy to see where the idea comes from: the mistaken belief that the only essential element in jazz is 'swing' and, consequently, "it don't mean a thing if it ain't got that swing"!

Certainly, many of Bill's more soulful performances were concerned less with rhythm than with the harmonic possibilities of the number he was playing; and if that were all there was to his style, this criticism might have carried some weight. But the simple fact is — as the briefest dip into any one of his sadly too few albums will show — when the occasion demands, his incisive left hand punches and sparkling right hand flurries, working in total sympathy with a hard-driving bass line, demonstrate an unquestionable ability to swing with the best.

In this book, we have set out to give you a taste of both sides of the work of this deeply serious and extraordinarily gifted musician.

You'll find a few minor flaws. Like every jazz player that ever lived, he didn't always hit the note or chord intended. (There's a simple explanation: the brain works faster than the fingers. Much faster!) But, contrary to the assertions of some critics, his technique was unquestionably superb. It's just that he didn't make it his first priority. He was too introspective, too interested in the music itself to indulge in irrelevant braggadocio.

His taste, however, seemed to lead him towards a quieter, more reflective approach. He probes, examines, discards what he considers irrelevant and develops what he considers to be the essential ingredients of a tune; ingredients which aren't always what you'd expect.

In other words, he sets out to create something totally new every time he plays. You could say that, more than almost any of the great stylists, his playing comes across not so much as the performance of a finished piece, but as the process of composition itself.

This probably explains why his repertoire was not as extensive as that of his contemporaries. He worked and re-worked the same numbers over and over, exploring their harmonic and melodic potential, finding new things each time and expressing them in ever more subtle ways. Sometimes this consists of paring down the left hand to almost nothing: an isolated rhythmic stab, apparently barely related to any underlying harmonic shape the improvisation might contain. Indeed, on occasions he dispenses with the left hand altogether for a chorus or so, leaving the bass to provide the ground on which to build his complex melodic lines. These lines are frequently formed by a conjuror-like unravelling of immense chord structures; often amazing, always impressive.

Above everything else, Bill Evans was an incredibly important innovator; especially (and despite what's just been said) where the left hand was concerned. Moving forward from the simple fourths and sevenths of the bebop era, he deconstructed the original harmonies, emptying and inverting the chords, leaving an accompaniment that was just as percussive but more relevant to what was happening in the right hand.

His influence on all subsequent piano jazz has been enormous. A huge percentage of what we hear today comes from what he did then.

So forget the critics. Jazz is music of the moment: a spontaneous development of melodic, harmonic and rhythmic ideas. By any definition, Bill Evans was a great exponent of this art.

AN INTRODUCTION BY EDITOR JACK LONG

AUTUMN LEAVES
(LES FEUILLES MORTES)

MUSIC BY JOSEPH KOSMA
WORDS BY JACQUES PREVERT

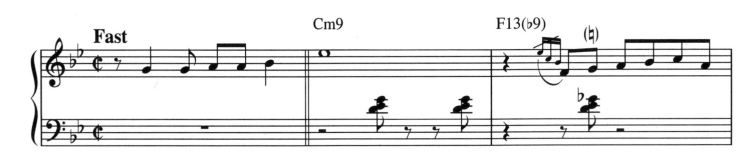

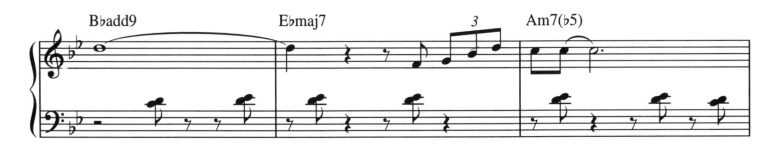

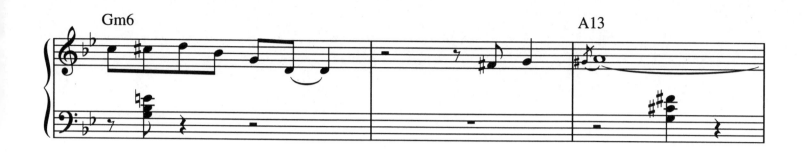

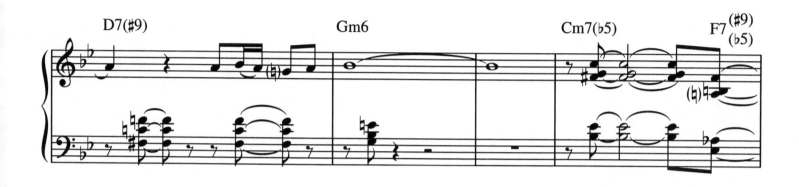

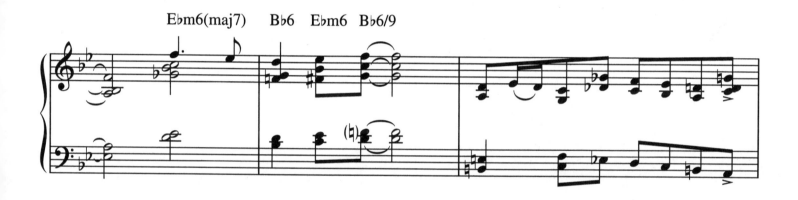

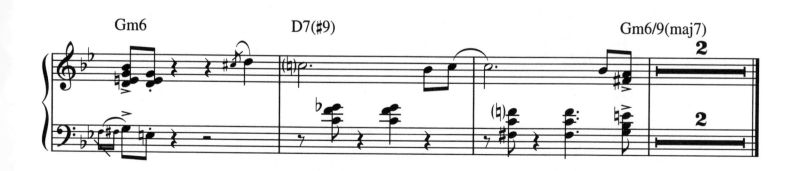

HOW MY HEART SINGS

BY EARL ZINDARS

Fast jazz waltz

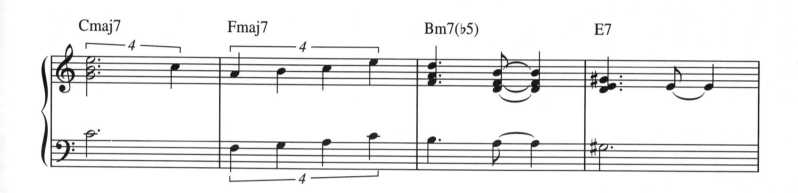

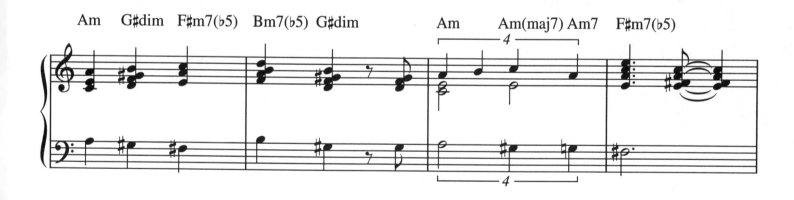

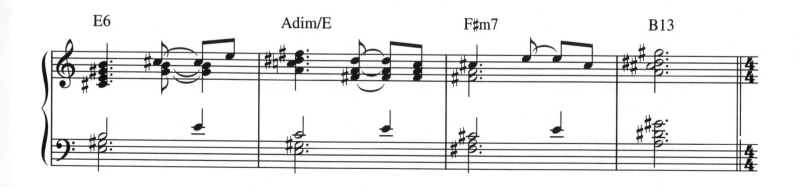

MINORITY
BY GIGI GRYCE

Medium fast

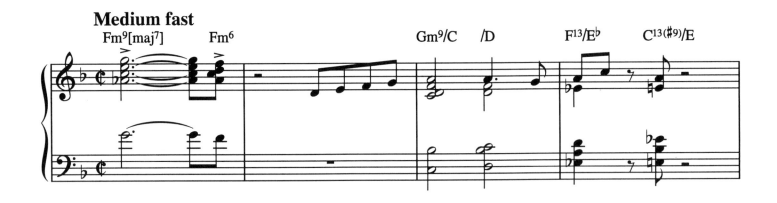

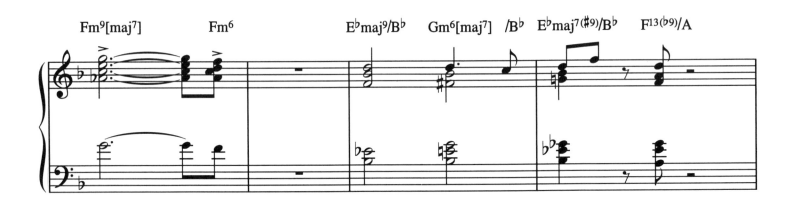

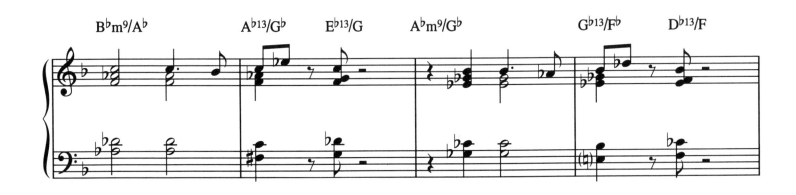

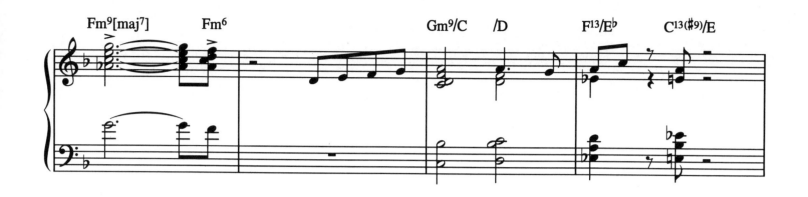

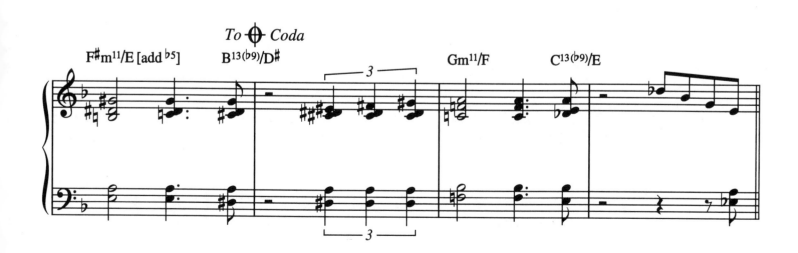

D.C. al Coda

CODA

Gm¹¹/F   C¹³⁽♭⁹⁾/E   Fm⁹[maj⁷]

MY FOOLISH HEART
WORDS & MUSIC BY NED WASHINGTON & VICTOR YOUNG

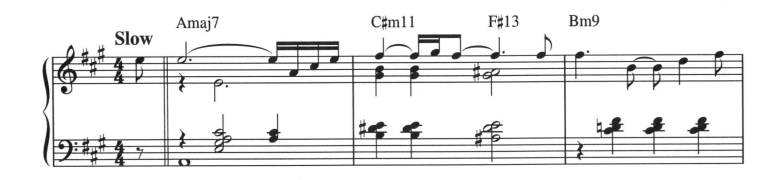

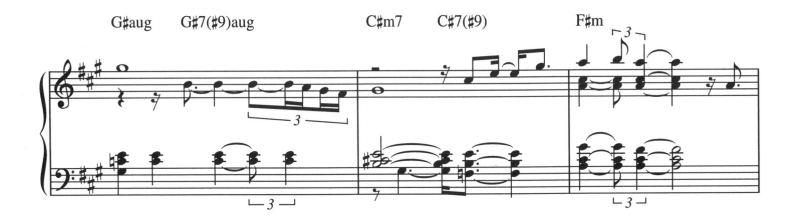

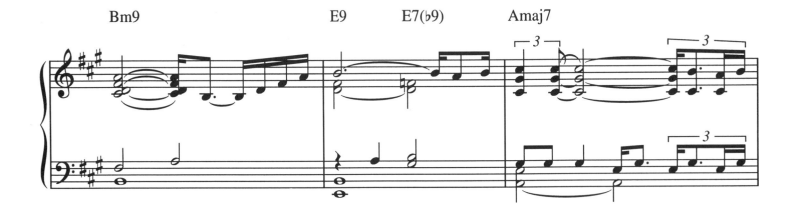

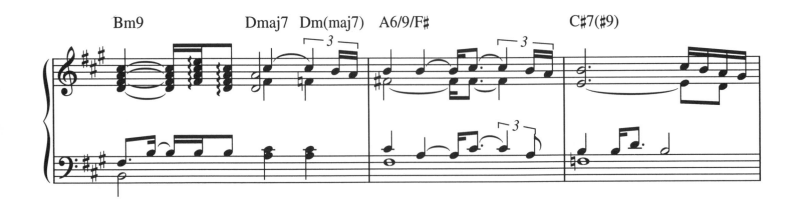

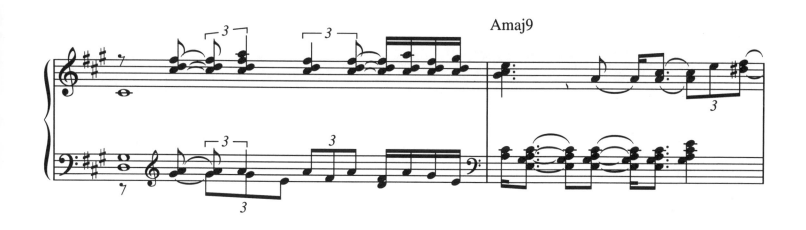

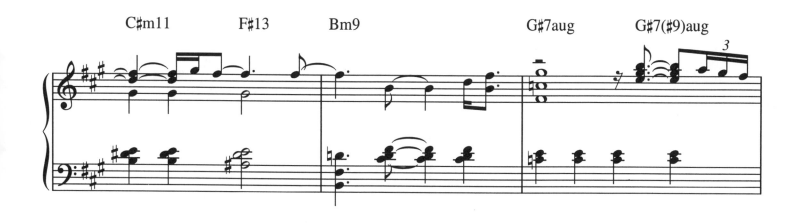

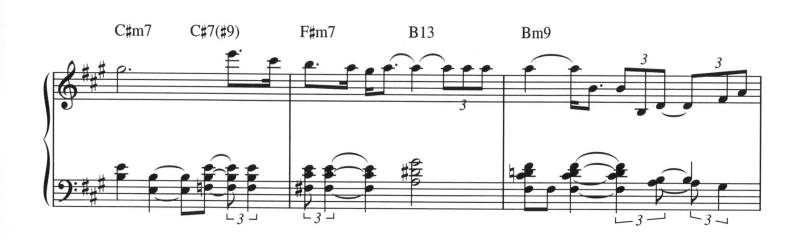

17

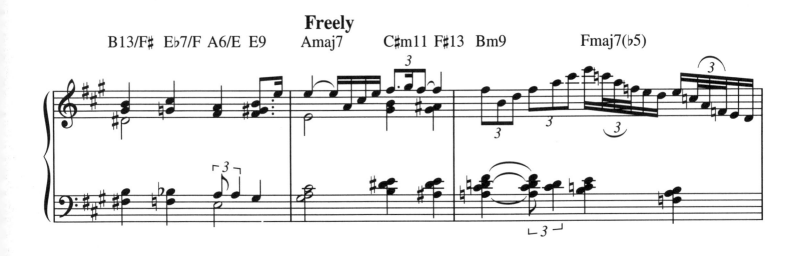

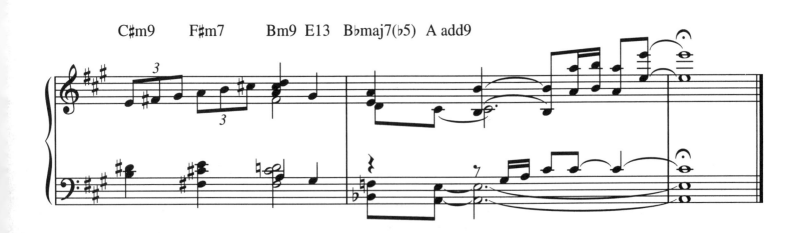

OLEO

BY SONNY ROLLINS

Very fast

N.C.

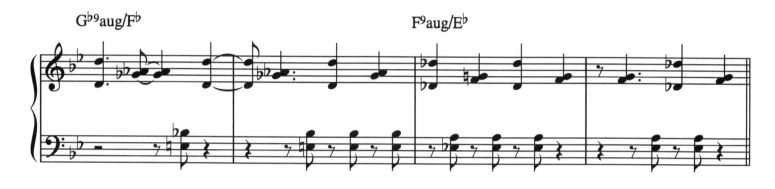

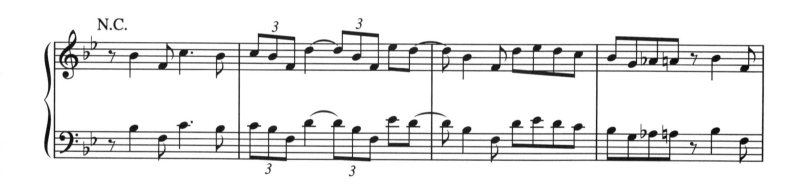

D.C. al Coda

PEACE PIECE

BY BILL EVANS

Medium slow: lyrically and freely

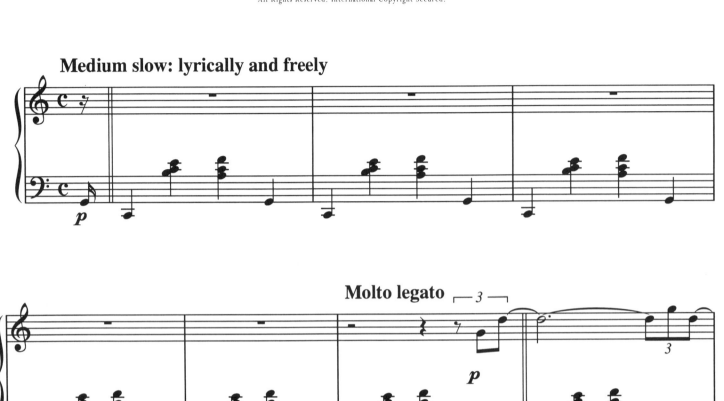

Molto legato

25

26

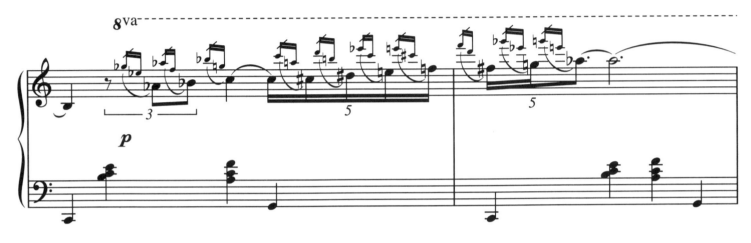

PEAU DOUCE

BY STEVE SWALLOW

Medium slow

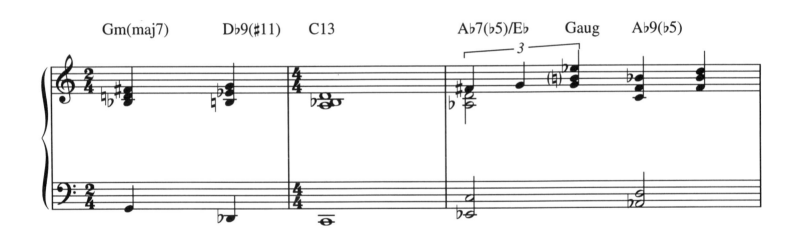

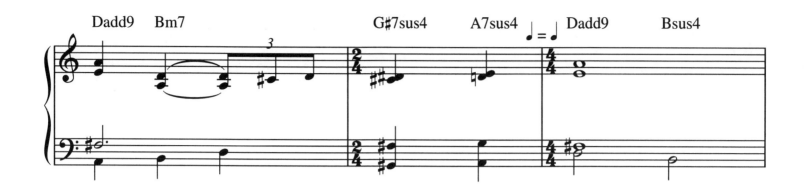

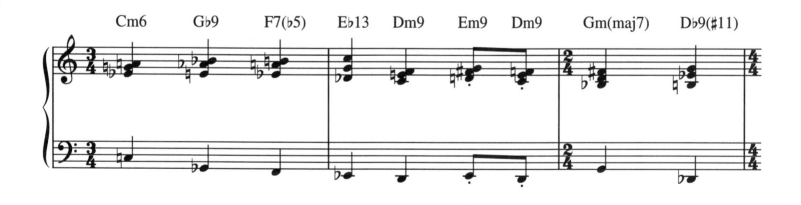

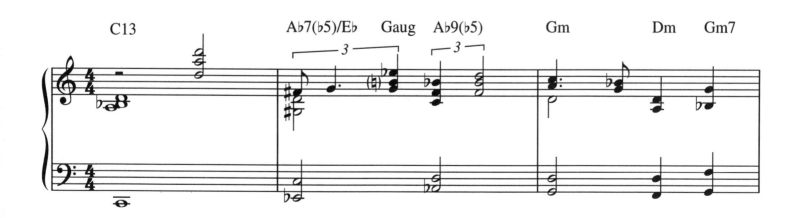

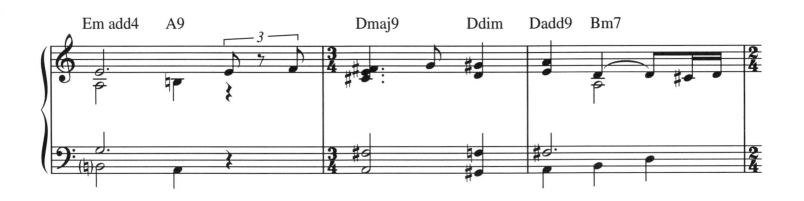

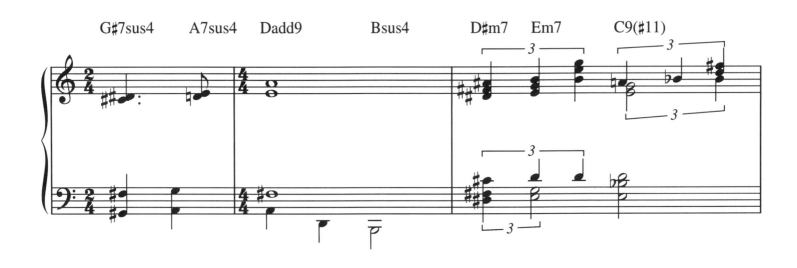

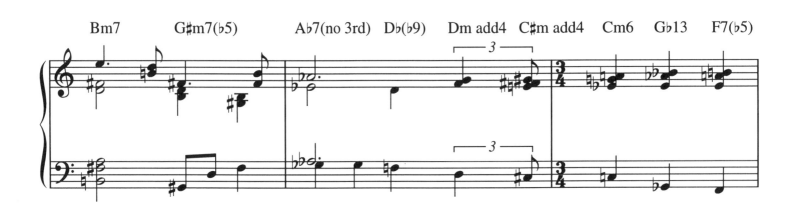

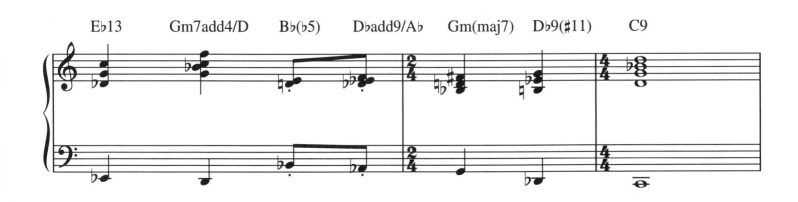

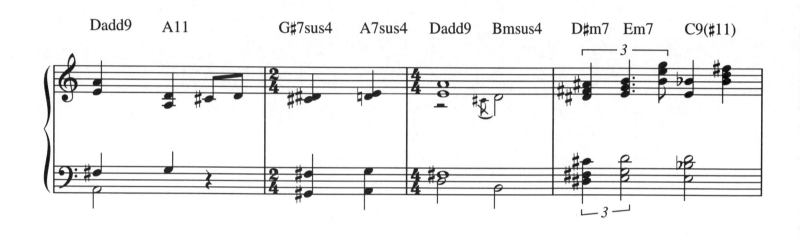

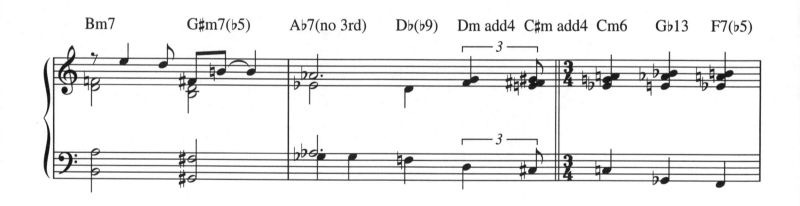

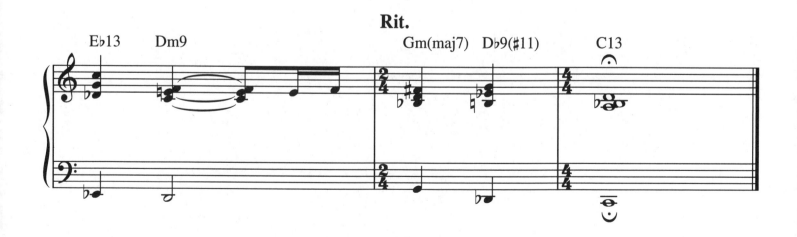

PERI'S SCOPE

BY BILL EVANS

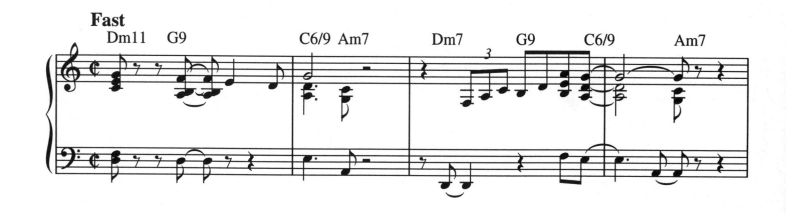

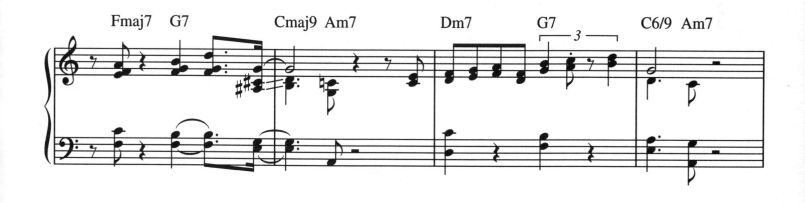

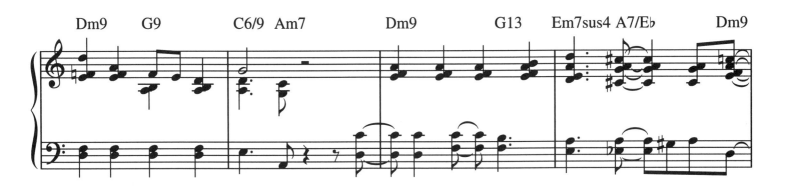

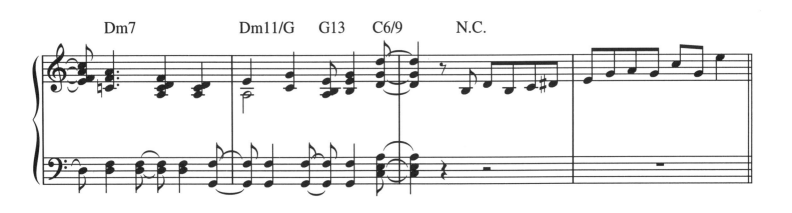

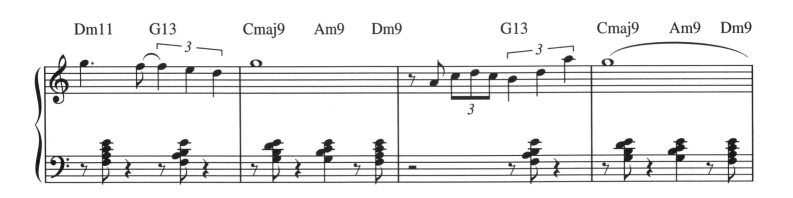

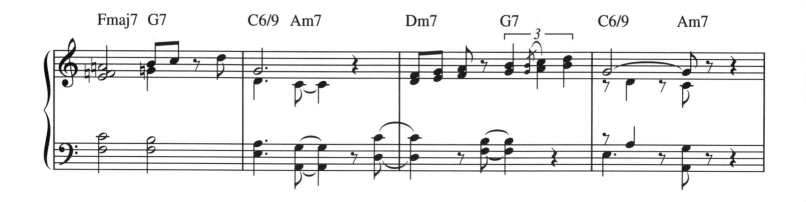

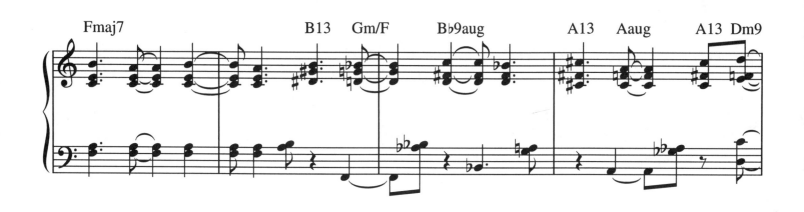

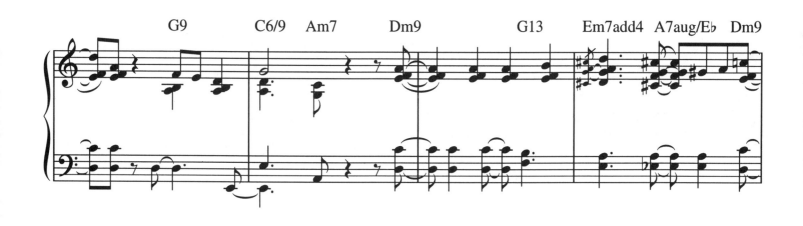

QUIET NOW

BY DENNY ZEITLIN

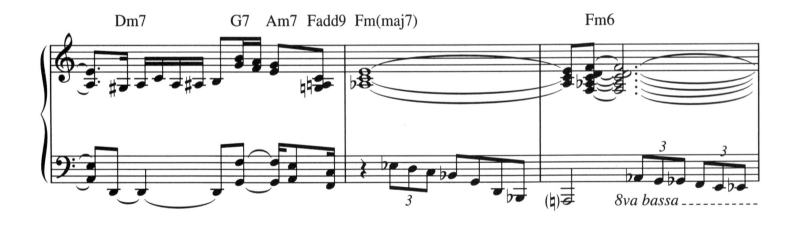

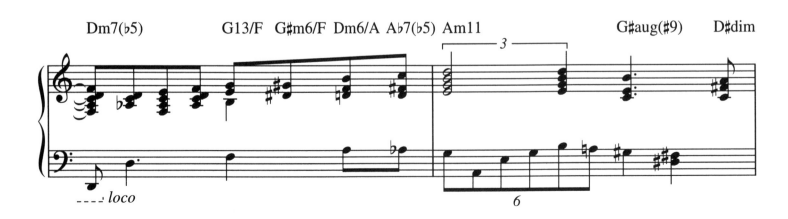

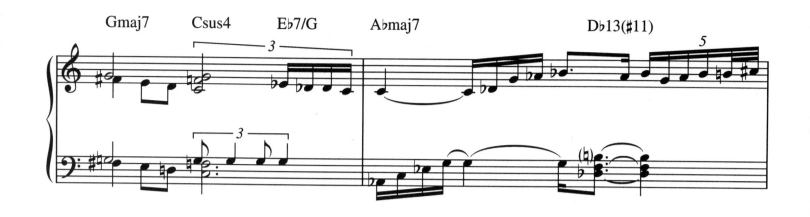

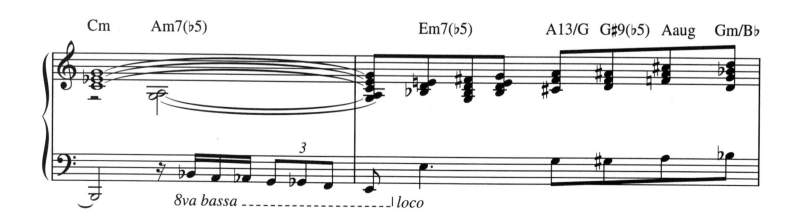

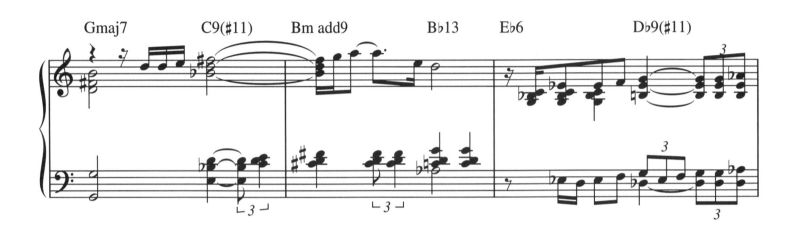

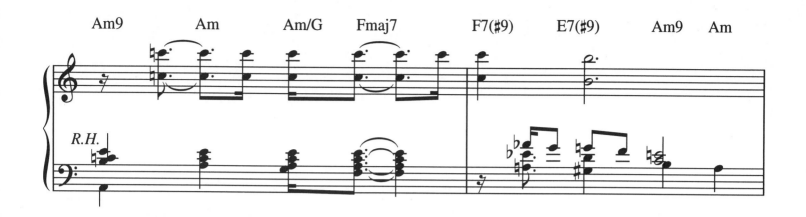

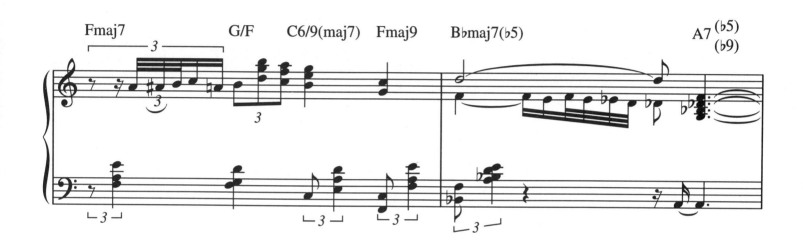

Molto rall.

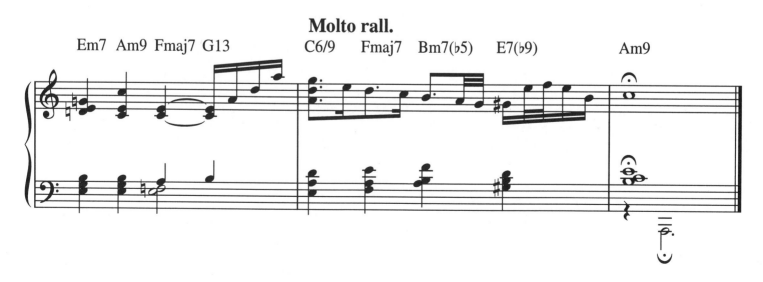

TWO LONELY PEOPLE

BY BILL EVANS

Medium 'ballad' tempo

Freely, espress.

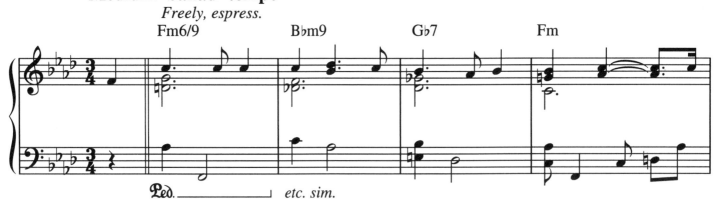

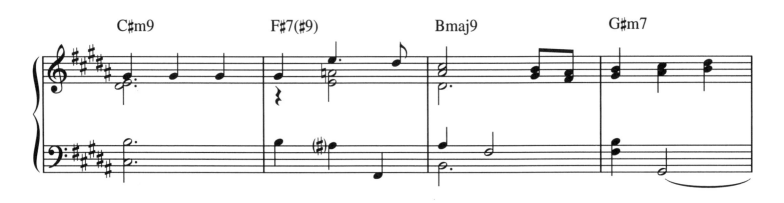

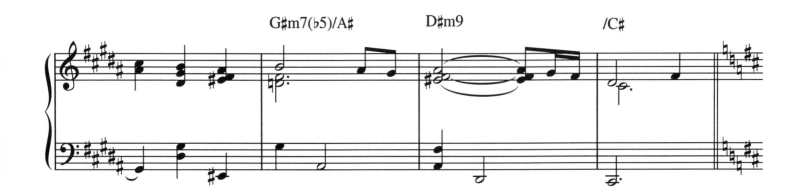

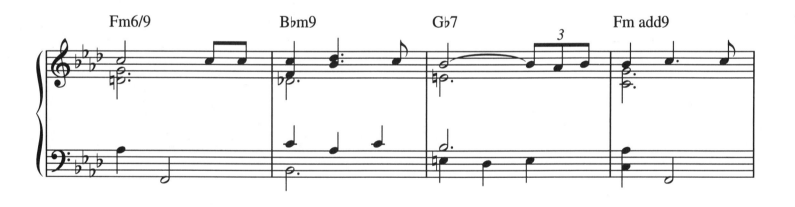

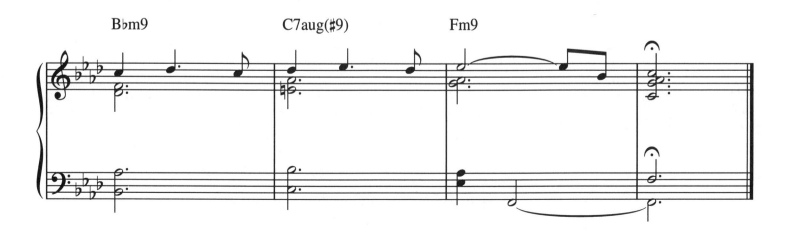

TIME REMEMBERED

BY BILL EVANS

Slow 'ballad' tempo

Freely, espress.

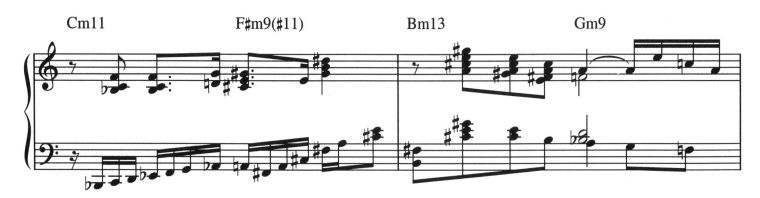

WALTZ FOR DEBBY

BY BILL EVANS

Fast jazz waltz

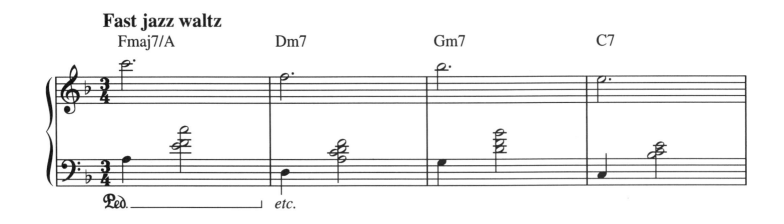

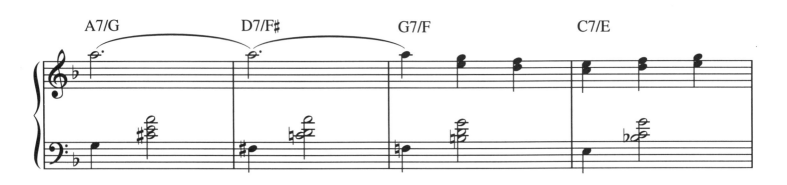

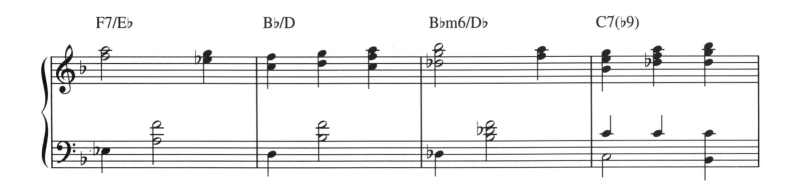

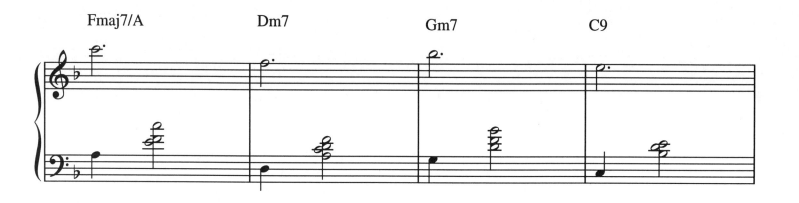

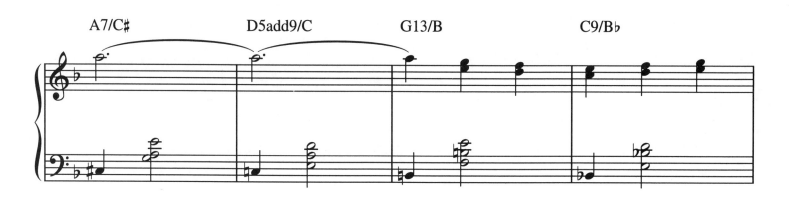

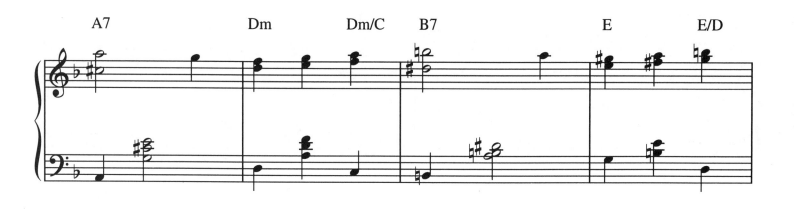

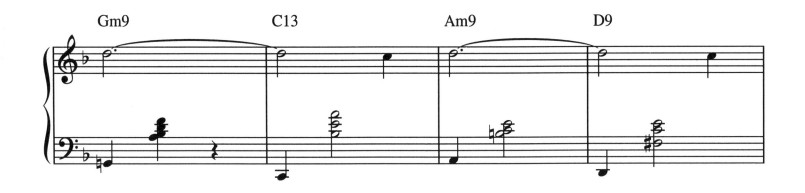

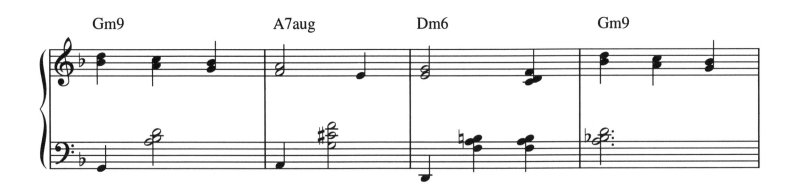

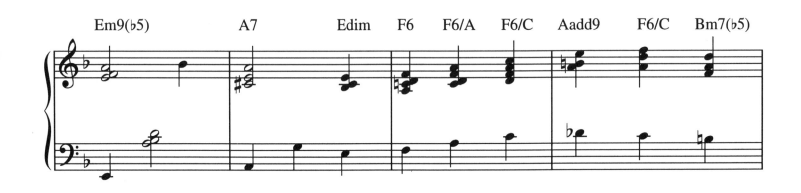

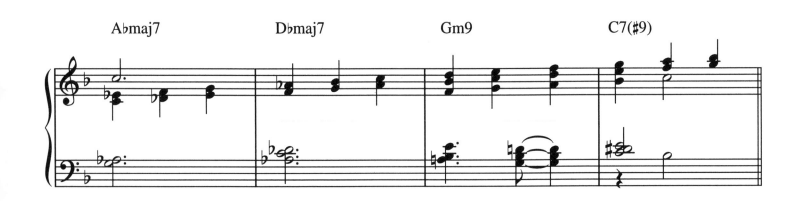

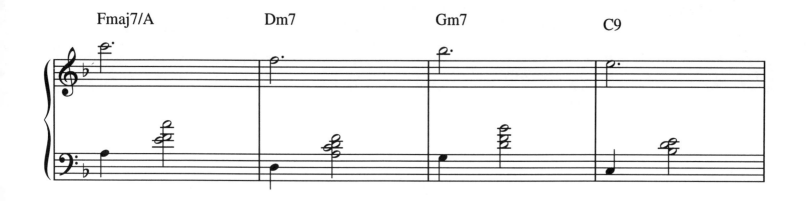

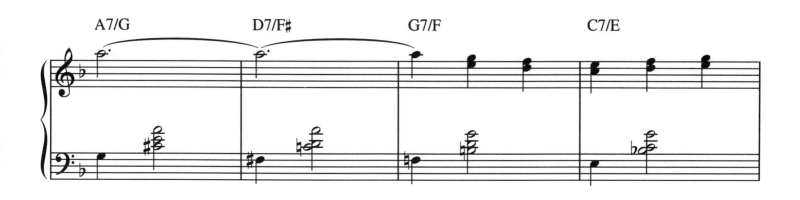

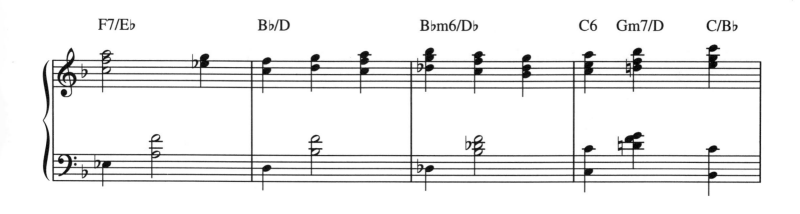

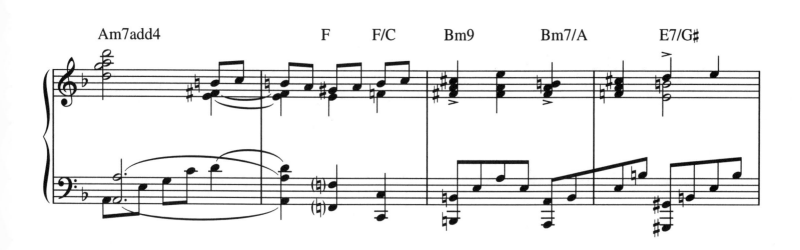

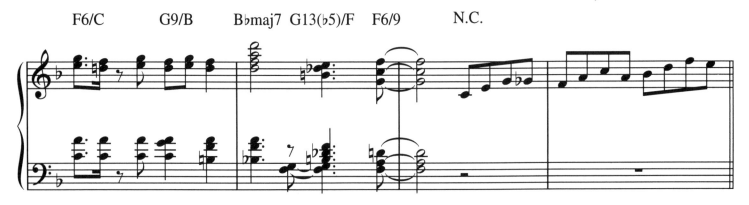

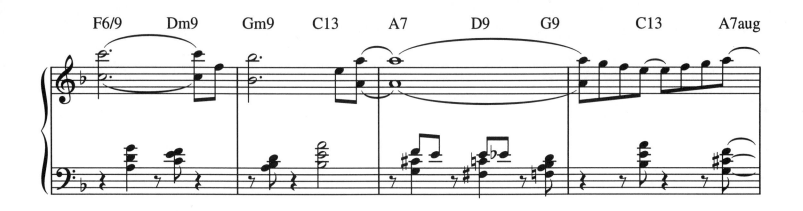

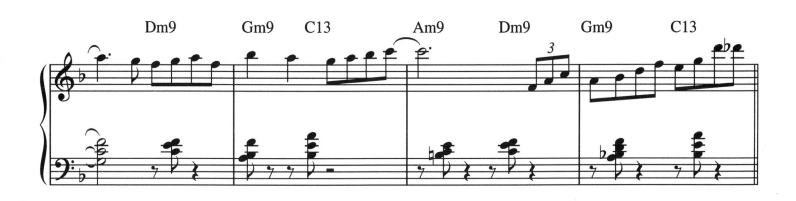

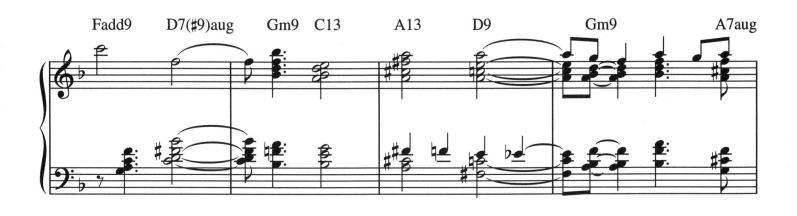

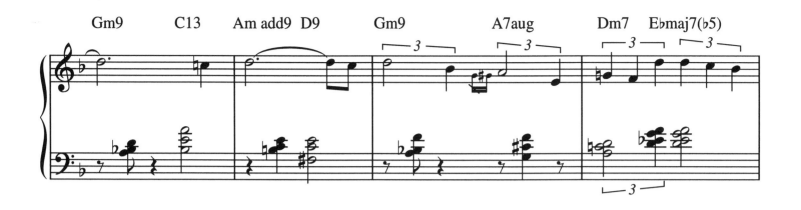

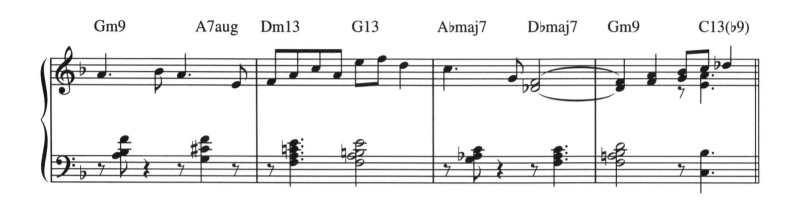

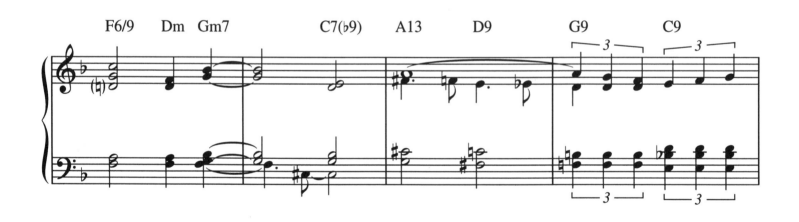

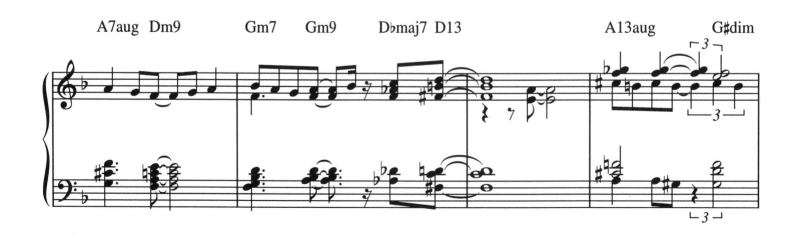

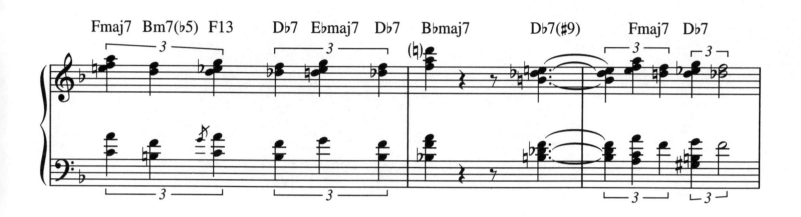

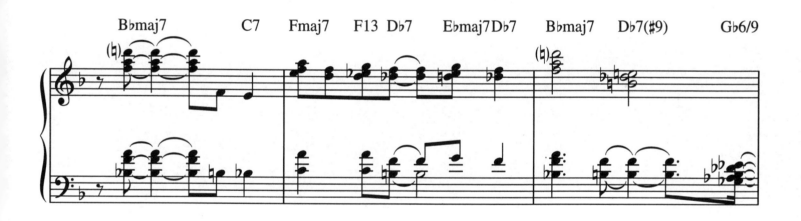

Molto rit.

WHO CAN I TURN TO?

WORDS & MUSIC BY LESLIE BRICUSSE & ANTHONY NEWLEY

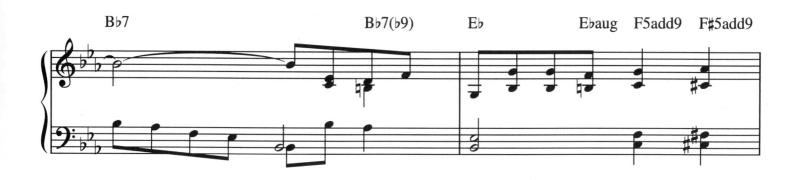

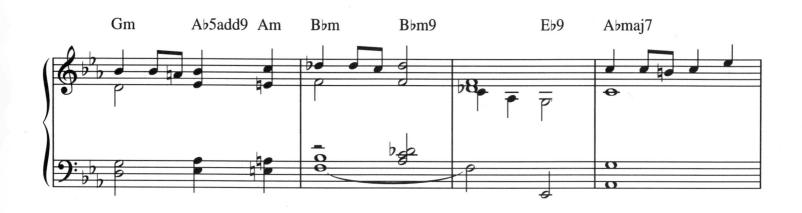

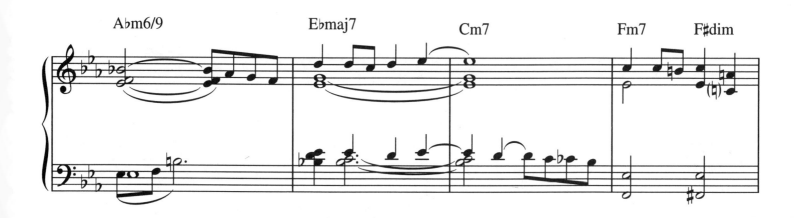

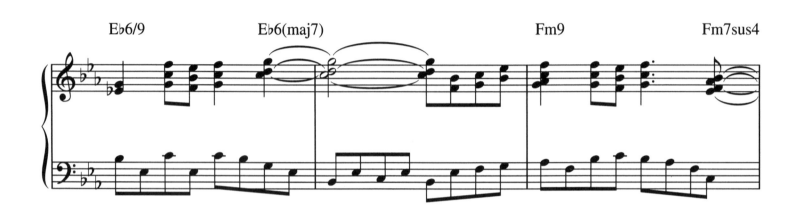

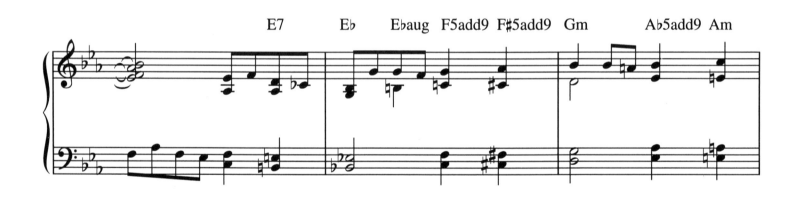

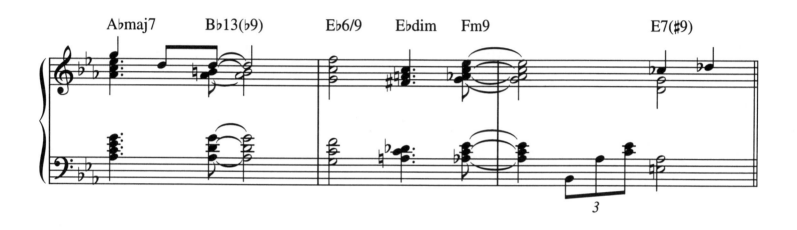

Medium tempo

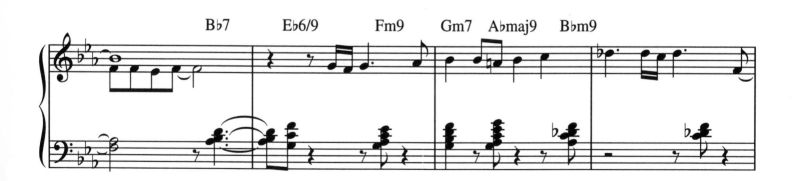

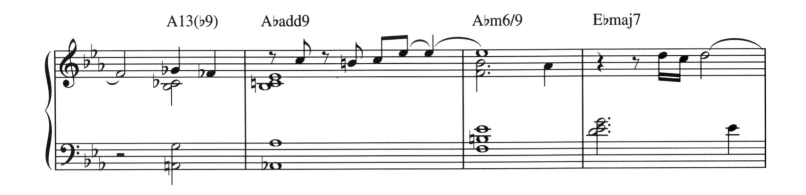

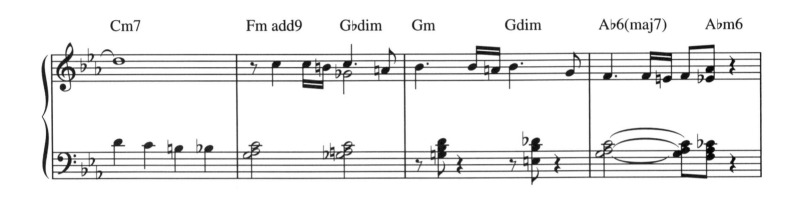

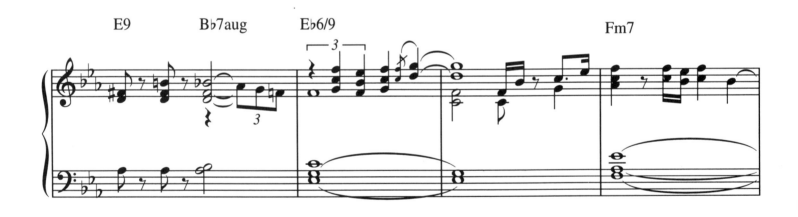

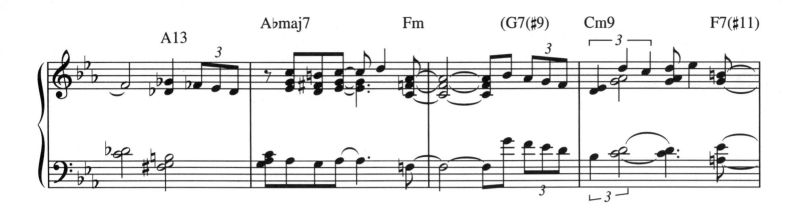

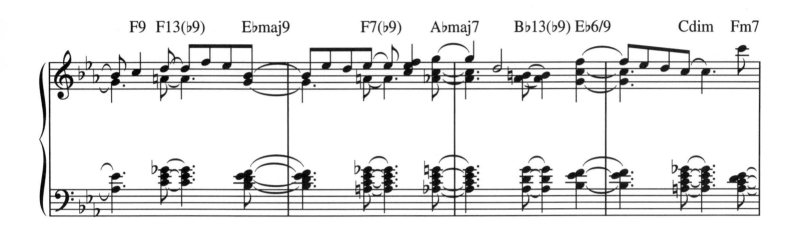

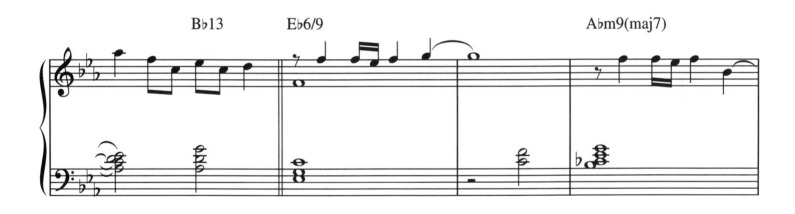

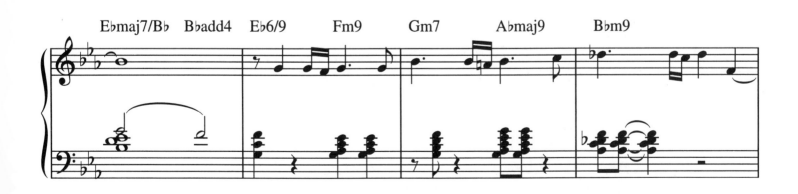

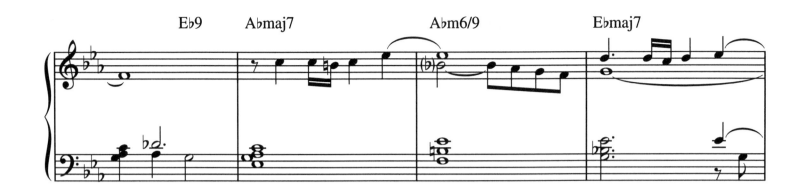

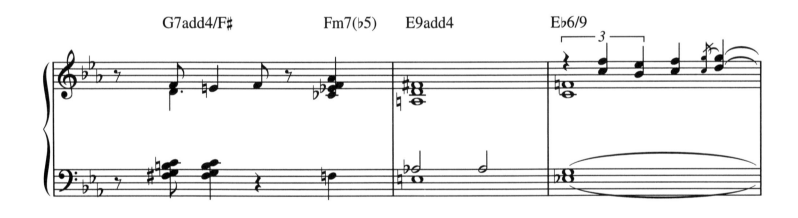

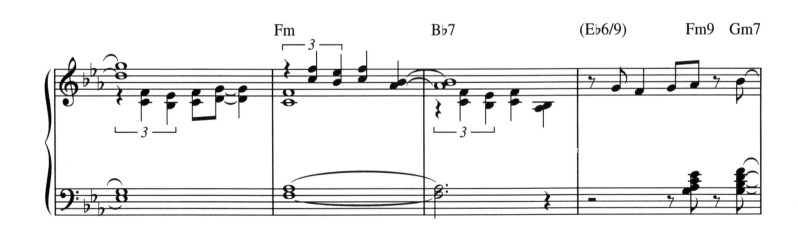

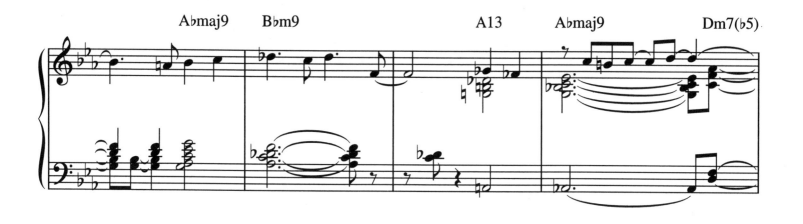

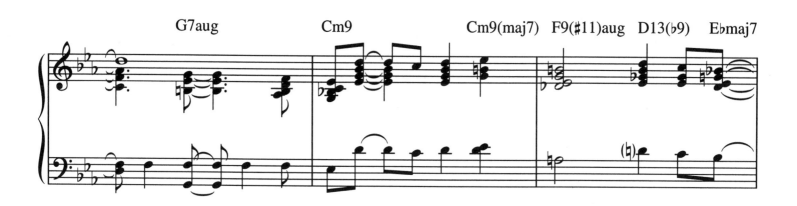

Freely

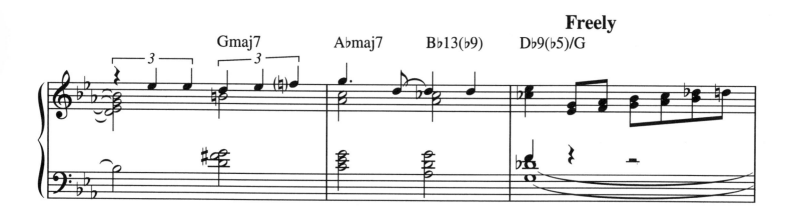

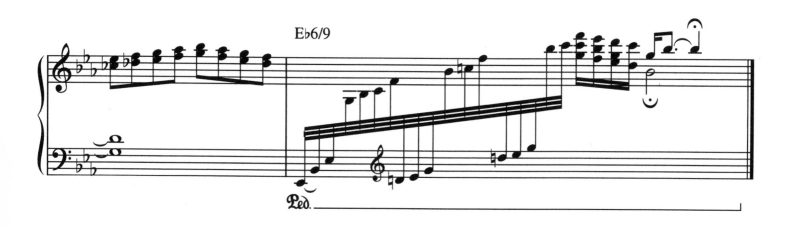

EPILOGUE

BY BILL EVANS

Medium tempo: freely

Printed by Printwise (Haverhill) Limited, Suffolk   11/06 (60413)